DAVID MERRICK

presents

HELLO, DOLLY!

A Musical Comedy

Book by
MICHAEL STEWART

Music and Lyrics by
JERRY HERMAN

Based on "THE MATCHMAKER" by THORNTON WILDER

Settings Designed by OLIVER SMITH

Costumes by FREDDY WITTOP

Lighting by JEAN ROSENTHAL

Musical Direction and Vocal Arrangements by SHEPARD COLEMAN

Orchestrations by PHILIP J. LANG

Dance and Incidental Music Arranged by PETER HOWARD

Directed and Choreographed by
GOWER CHAMPION

VOCAL SCORE

Piano Reduction by Robert H. Noeltner

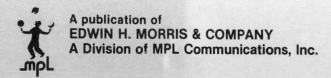

A publication of
EDWIN H. MORRIS & COMPANY
A Division of MPL Communications, Inc.

mpL

FIRST PERFORMANCE AT THE ST. JAMES THEATRE, NEW YORK
JANUARY 16, 1964

CAST OF CHARACTERS
(In order of appearance)

MRS. DOLLY GALLAGHER LEVI	Carol Channing
ERNESTINA	Mary Jo Catlett
AMBROSE KEMPER	Igors Gavon
HORSE	Jan LaPrade, Bonnie Mathis
HORACE VANDERGELDER	David Burns
ERMENGARDE	Alice Playten
CORNELIUS HACKL	Charles Nelson Reilly
BARNABY TUCKER	Jerry Dodge
IRENE MOLLOY	Eileen Brennan
MINNIE FAY	Sondra Lee
MRS. ROSE	Amelia Haas
RUDOLPH	David Hartman
JUDGE	Gordon Connell
COURT CLERK	Ken Ayers

Townspeople, Waiters, Etc.:

Nicole Barth, Monica Carter, Carvel Carter, Amelia Haas, Jan LaPrade, Joan Buttons Leonard, Paula Lloyd, Marilyne Mason, Bonnie Mathis, Yolanda Poropat, Bonnie Schon, Barbara Sharma, Mary Ann Snow, Jamie Thomas, Pat Trott, Mickey Wayland, Ken Ayers, Alvin Beam, Joel Craig, Dick Crowley, Gene Gebauer, Joe Helms, Richard Hermany, Neil Jones, Charles Karel, Paul Kastl, Jim Maher, Joe McWherter, John Mineo, Randy Phillips, Lowell Purvis, Michael Quinn, Will Roy, Paul Solen, Ronnie Young.

SCENES

ACT ONE

Scene 1: Along Fourth Avenue, New York City.

Scene 2: Grand Central Station.

Scene 3: A Street in Yonkers.

Scene 4: Vandergelder's Hay and Feed Store, Yonkers.

Scene 5: The Yonkers Depot.

Scene 6: Outside Mrs. Molloy's Hat Shop—Water Street, New York City.

Scene 7: Inside the Hat Shop.

Scene 8: A Quiet Street.

Scene 9: 14th Street.

ACT TWO

Scene 1: In front of the Hoffman House Hotel, on Fifth Avenue.

Scene 2: Outside the Harmonia Gardens Restaurant, on the Battery.

Scene 3: Inside the Harmonia Gardens Restaurant.

Scene 4: Tableaux Vivantes.

Scene 5: A Courtroom on Centre Street.

Scene 6: The Hay and Feed Store, Yonkers.

Applications for performance of this work, whether legitimate, stock, amateur, or foreign should be addressed to

TAMS-WITMARK MUSIC LIBRARY Inc.

757 Third Avenue   New York 17, N. Y.

ORCHESTRA INSTRUMENTATION:

Reed I—Piccolo, Flute, Clarinet and Alto Saxophone   Reed III—Clarinet and Tenor Saxophone

Reed II—Clarinet and Alto Saxophone   Reed IV—Clarinet, Bass Clarinet and Baritone Saxophone

3 Trumpets	Violins I & II	Cello	2 Percussion
2 Trombones	Viola	Bass	Piano-Celeste
			Guitar-Banjo

Orchestra parts are cued so the score may be played with the following minimum number of parts: 3 Reeds, 2 Trumpets, 1 Trombone, 1 Percussion, Bass and Piano. Add parts in the following order to build the full Orchestra: Reed IV, Trombone II, Trumpet III, Cello, Violins, Viola, Percussion II, and Guitar-Banjo.

MUSICAL NUMBERS

The original Broadway production performed without an Overture

HELLO, DOLLY!

David Burns and Carol Channing

Left to right:
Sondra Lee,
Carol Channing,
Eileen Brennan.

Charles Nelson Reilly, Eileen Brennan, Jerry Dodge, Sondra Lee

David Burns, Mary Jo Catlett.

Eileen Brennan

Charles Nelson Reilly, Carol Channing, Alice Playten, Igors Gavon.

Alice Playten, Igors Gavon

Sondra Lee, Jerry Dodge

HELLO, DOLLY !

Carol Channing

HELLO, DOLLY!

Music and Lyrics by JERRY HERMAN

OVERTURE

JERRY HERMAN

1129

1129

Segue as one to
Opening, Act I

The Original Broadway Production performed without an Overture

HELLO, DOLLY!

JERRY HERMAN

No. 1

Opening Act I

(Mm. ♩ = 120)
Briskly - in 2

Piano

ff Tutti

1129

No. 2   I Put My Hand In

cue: DOLLY: .... some sew---I meddle!

DOLLY: Ad. lib.

I have al-ways been a wom-an who ar-rang-es things, For the

pleas-ure and the pro-fit it de - rives.   I have al-ways been a wom-an who ar-

rang-es things -- Like fur-ni-ture and daf-fo-dils and lives.

12

push, sort of freeze

30

needs a lit - tle push! So, I put my hand in here.

I put my hand in there.

40

And a girl o - ver six foot three

Loves a man who comes up to her ear,

14

Sure - ly, it's ob - vi - ous she'll nev - er be se - duced Till some kind soul con - de - scends to give her beau a lit - tle boost! So, I put my hand in there. I put my hand in here.

gin to fidg-et. Then I clench my palm, The preach-er reads a

Trbs., Cello

197

psalm, When I put my hand in

Vlns.

Tutti

201 Più mosso

there!

ff

Tutti

W.W., Vlns.

(Br. Pyramid)

R.H.

Ped.

Segue as one

No. 2a

Yonkers March

Piano

Fade out as Vandergelder speaks.

cue to start vamp: HORACE:...which, in Yonkers, is about as far as you can go!
cue to stop vamp: HORACE: ..the answer is simple ...

cue to sing: HORACE: ..and pretty dirty, too!

ALL:

dump-ing the ash - es. Yes, it takes a wom-an, A

dain - ty wom-an, A sweet-heart, a mis-tress, a

wife. Oh yes, it takes a wom-an, a

frag - ile wom-an To bring you the sweet things in

No. 3a   It Takes A Woman-Reprise

34

No. 4   Put On Your Sunday Clothes

Cue: BARNABY: Yes, Cornelius! Yes!
cue: DOLLY:
Now, the first thing
to do....

Cue: DOLLY:
chicken for eight o'
clock tonight! Hah!

Cue:CORNELIUS: We're
going to New York!
(Explosions)   Freely
CORNELIUS:

Fade out on cue:DOLLY:
..my card..

(Barnaby slams
trap door)

Out there,

Piano

There's a world out-side of Yon-kers,   'Way out there be-yond this

hick town, Barn-a-by,   There's a slick town, Barn-a-by.

tine and dime ci - gars. We're gon-na find ad-

ven - ture in the eve - ning air, ___ Girls in white_ in a

per - fumed night_ Where the lights are bright_ as the stars!

Put on your Sun - day clothes, we're gon - na ride through town ___

Put on your Sun - day clothes when you feel down and out.

Strut down the street and have your pic - ture took.

Dressed like a dream, your spir-its seem to turn a - bout. That

Be-neath your par - a - sol the world is all a smile

that makes you feel brand new down to your toes. _____ Get

out your feath - ers, your pat - ent leath - ers, Your beads and buck - les and

bows   For there's no blue Mon-day   in your Sun-day   clothes.

Be-neath your bow - ler   brim   the world's a   sim - ple   song.

No. 4a Put On Your Sunday Clothes-Encore

No. 4b

Incidental
(Hat Shop)

No. 5   Ribbons Down My Back

N.B. An optional measure for Celeste (C7 arpeg. in tempo)
may be added before bar one.

No. 5a   Ribbons Down My Back-Reprise

No. 6   Motherhood March

Cue: DOLLY: I know what I stand for!

on the bridge at Wa - ter - loo, 'Neath that great tri - um - phal

arch? _____ If you hear him sing - ing "Dix - ie" in the

sug - ar cane, Stand up and march, march,

march! I stand for

68

No. 7

Dancing

cue: DOLLY: Let's go back to Lesson One.

74

No. 7a

Incidental
(I Put My Hand In)

No. 8   Before The Parade Passes By

12 Moderately - in 2

Bells, Fl., Vlns.

W.W.

mp

Tbn. (cup), Gtr., Cello pizz. (cued for BS.)

W.W., Vlns.

(cued for Fl. 8va.) Vlns.

+Br. Muted

mf

pp

+Trb.

20 MRS. MOLLOY: Mrs. Levi, come along. . . . .etc.

Cls. (sust.)
Trbn., Gtr.
Cello

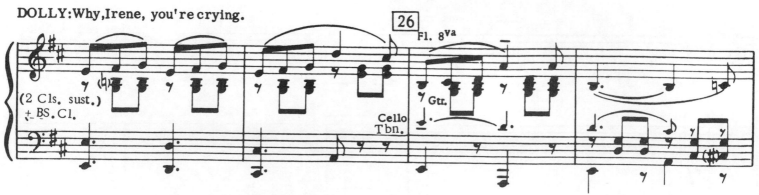

DOLLY: Why, Irene, you're crying.

26 Fl. 8va

(2 Cls. sust.)
+ BS. Cl.

Cello
Tbn.

Gtr.

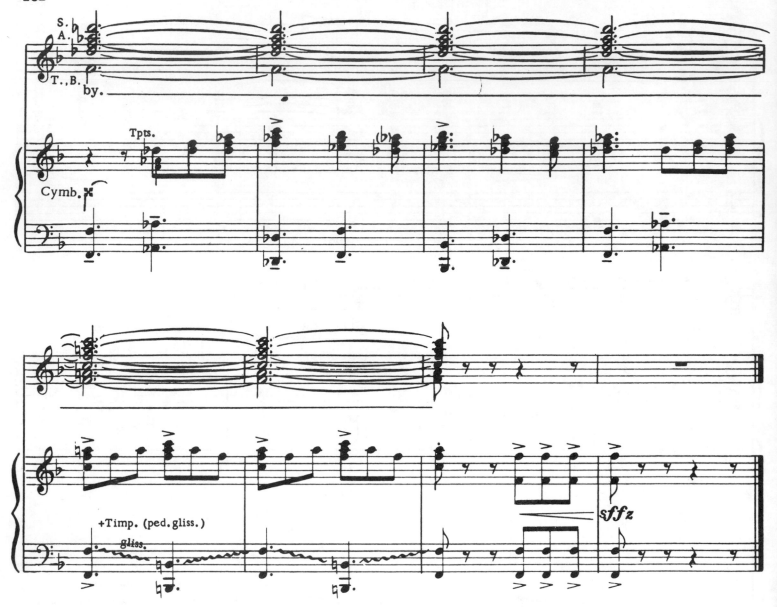

No. 9   Finale-Act I

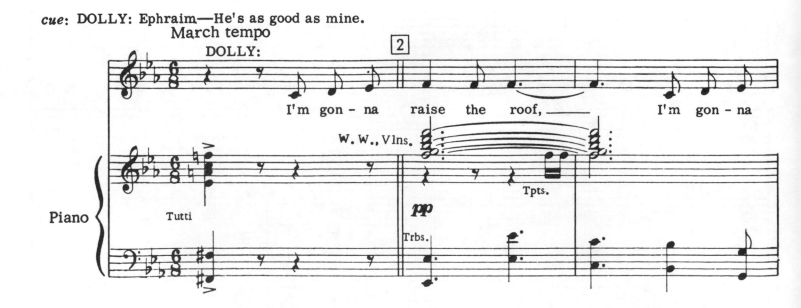

cue: DOLLY: Ephraim—He's as good as mine.

End Act I

No. 10

Entr'acte

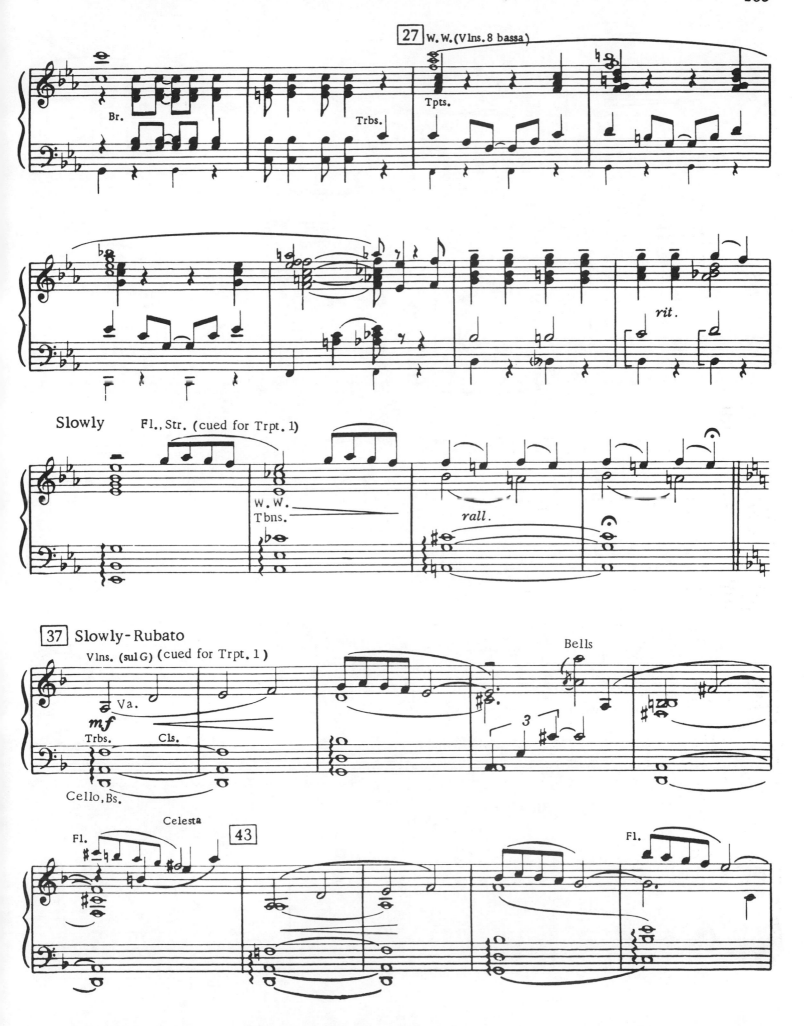

No. 11   Elegance

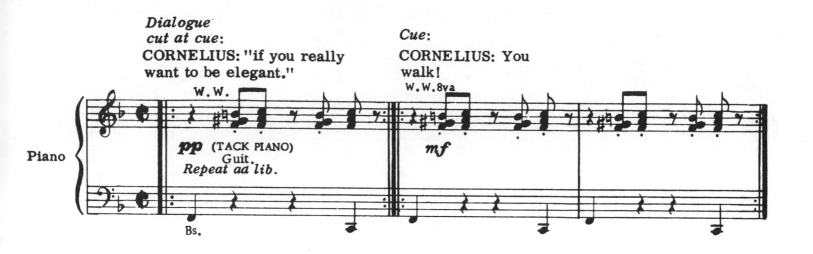

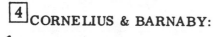

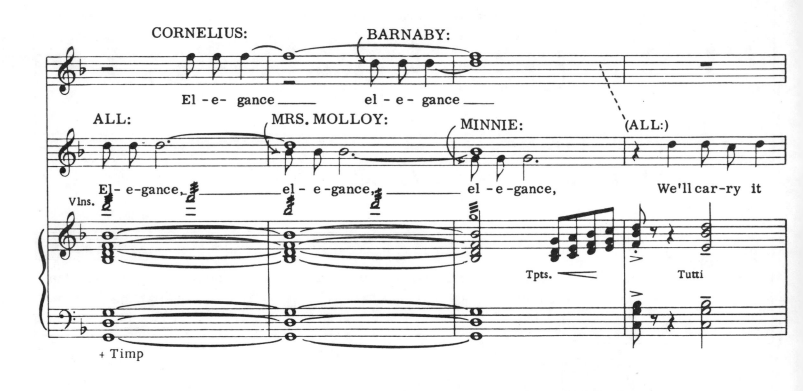

No. 11a   March To Harmonia Gardens

cue: MRS. MOLLOY: ..... a corset is a corset.

L'istesso tempo *(AMBROSE and ERMENGARDE enter)*

Repeat ad lib. until cue:
AMBROSE: Faster
-----That's it!

ERNESTINA: Sweet Ros - ie O' - Gra - dy! My sweet lit - tle rose. ___

cue: ERNESTINA and HORACE exit.

Br. muted

Str. pizz. +W.W.

Vamp ad lib. -Fade out as Rudolph barks out orders.

Bs.Cl., Cello

Bs.

No. 12   Waiters' Galop

Cue: RUDOLPH: ... or else!

RUDOLPH: -- I trust you are finding.... etc.

128

130

No. 12a

Hello, Dolly-Agitato

Cue: RUDOLPH: She just stepped out of her carriage!

No. 13   Hello, Dolly

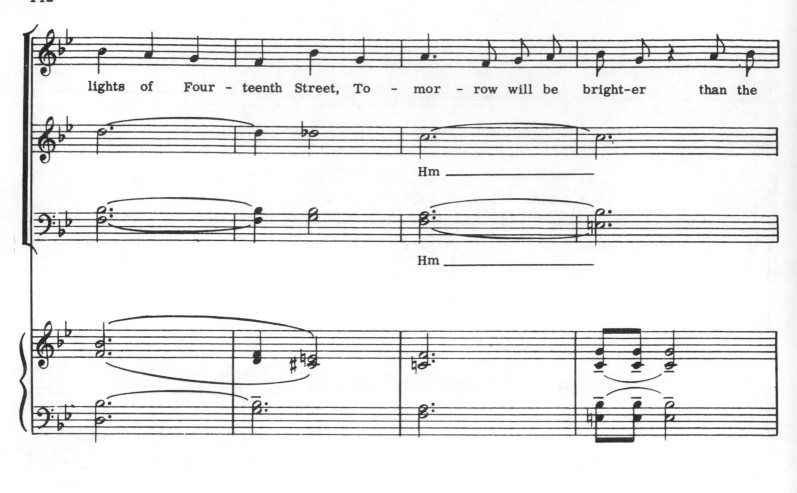

lights of Four-teenth Street, To - mor - row will be bright-er than the

Hm

Hm

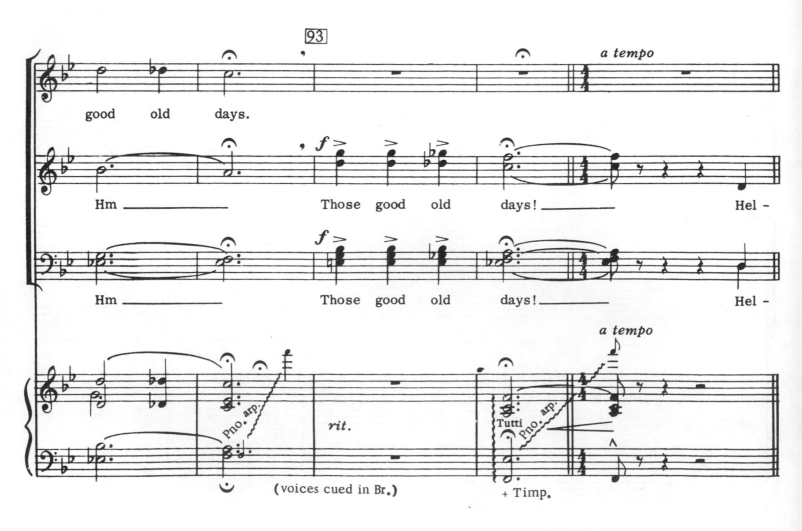

good old days.

Hm _____ Those good old days! _____ Hel -

Hm _____ Those good old days! _____ Hel -

(voices cued in Br.) + Timp.

No. 13a   Hello, Dolly-Encore

No. 14

Waiters' Galop-Reprise

Cue: DOLLY: There's someone in the dance com-
petition I particular want you to see.

No. 15

Polka

Cue: DOLLY: You can't go now.

Ad lib.
DOLLY: About to
begin---

Cue: HORACE: My
purse, I've lost my
purse.

Cont. at cue: DOLLY:
graceful movement--

No. 16   It Only Takes A Moment

Cue: MINNIE FAY: A -- a moment!

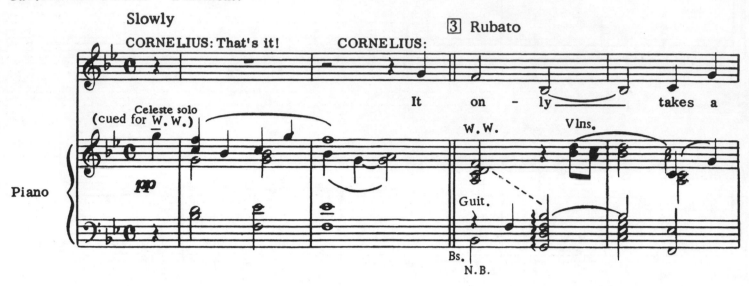

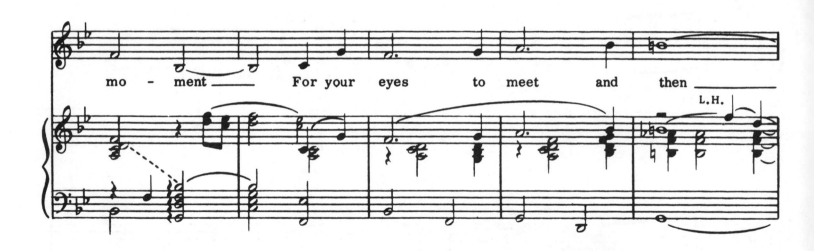

N.B. optional - Celeste solo to bar 7
Orchestra enters on "eyes"

162

Slowly

35 CORNELIUS: Isn't the world full of wonderful things? .... etc.

No. 16a It Only Takes A Moment-Part II

Cue: CLERK: Right after "It only--"

No. 16b   End Of Courtroom Scene

cue: JUDGE:.....Go, go---

No. 17   So Long, Dearie

cue: DOLLY:.....all I wanted to say to you was---

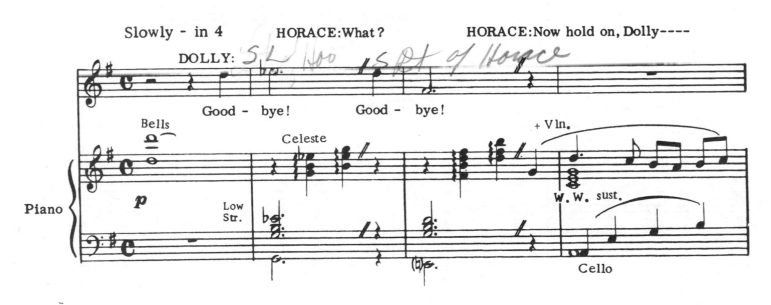

No. 17a   Change Of Scene

cue: *DOLLY exits*:

HORACE: And-

--and---I wouldn't marry you, Dolly Levi.....etc.

No. 18

Finale Ultimo

all a smile.

149

That makes you feel brand new down to your

toes. Get

Trbs.

157

out your feath - ers your pat - ent leath - ers, Your

(GIRLS sing melody – MEN divisi)

Dol – ly, It's so nice to have you back where you be – long.

So,

Dol – ly – 'll nev – er go a – way___ a –

gain.

Segue

No. 19   Curtain Music

(Hello, Dolly)

No. 20

Exit Music